TO THE ZOO

Consultant Gussie Hearsey on behalf of the Pre-school Playgroups Association
©1987 Maureen Roffey
Four Winds Press
Macmillan Publishing Company
866 Third Avenue, New York, NY 10022
First published 1987 in Great Britain by Walker Books Ltd, London
First American Edition 1988
Printed in Hong Kong by Dai Nippon (H.K.) Ltd.

10 9 8 7 6 5 4 3 2 1

Library of Congress Cataloging-in-Publication Data
Roffey, Maureen.
I spy at the zoo.
Summary: Readers may finish sentences by saying what
they "spy" in pictures of a visit to the zoo.
[1. Zoos—Fiction] I. Title.
PZ7.R6255Iad 1988   [E]   87-12116
ISBN 0-02-777150-4

I SPY
At the Zoo

Maureen Roffey

FOUR WINDS PRESS · NEW YORK

I spy the entrance to the zoo.

I spy a keeper with a bucket of . . .

9

I spy two black and white...

I spy a leopard lying on a…

I spy a giraffe reaching for...

I spy a tiger with five...

I spy a crocodile resting on a...

I spy an elephant squirting…

BIRD HOUSE

I spy a monkey swinging on a...

I spy a boy and girl riding...

Penguins

Pandas

Snakes

DO NOT FEED

I spy a seal swimming in a...

I spy our car. It's time to go home.

TO THE ZOO